D1190761

BECOMING
A MAN

A FATHER & SON JOURNEY TOGETHER

ROBERT LEWIS

LifeWay Press®

ISBN: 1415852626

Dewey Decimal Classification Number: 305.31
Subject Heading: MEN \ YOUNG MEN \ FATHERS AND SONS

Scripture taken from the *New American Standard Bible*®, Copyright ©
1960, 1962, 1963, 1968, 1971, 1972, 1973, 1975, 1977, 1995 by the
Lockman Foundation. Used by permission. (*www.lockman.org*)

Printed in the United States of America

Student Ministry Publishing
LifeWay Church Resources
One LifeWay Plaza
Nashville, Tennessee 37234-0174

We believe the Bible has God for its author; salvation for its end; and truth, without any mixture
of error, for its matter and that all Scripture is totally true and trustworthy.
The 2000 statement of *The Baptist Faith and Message* is our doctrinal guideline.

CONTENTS

A WORD OF WELCOME

FEW THINGS ARE MORE IMPORTANT to a young man than having a clear vision of what it means to be a man. And few things are more empowering to a son than receiving that vision from his dad. Having had the privilege of doing that with both my sons, I know from experience the impact such a vision imparts. It's life changing!

The truth is, boys don't automatically become men by growing older. Boys must be guided to manhood. They need true masculinity spelled out for them.

Let me say that whether you are a son just now entering into manhood or a dad wanting to have a helpful part in that process, I am honored to be teamed with you over the coming six sessions. We're going to have fun while we explore what it means to be a man. We're also going to have a number of revealing discussions, and hopefully, in the end, we're going to all end up better men.

Sons, be aware these sessions are not dumbed down "boy stuff." I'm going to speak to you like a man and ask you to engage and interact with those in your group like a man. Step up to this challenge. This is a one-of-a-kind experience you are about to have with your dad. Make the most of it.

Dads, as we proceed in our journey together, many of the questions you will be asked to answer in the "Let's Talk It Over" time will require a good measure of honesty and transparency on your part. Don't shrink back from this. Be real! Speak more like a man than a dad to your son and to the group. Don't preach or lecture. Instead, let the group see the ups and downs of your own personal manhood journey. Everyone in the group will benefit from your openness.

Let me also mention that these video sessions on manhood are condensed and edited from a much larger video curriculum called "Men's Fraternity." Your sessions are the best of that series pertaining to good father-son interaction.

Are you ready to begin? I sincerely believe that on the other end of our adventure together, you will find yourself embracing a clear vision of manhood and rejoicing that you did this together as father and son!

—Robert Lewis

SESSION 1

The Four Faces of Manhood

I. MANHOOD'S FOUR FACES

    A. FACE ONE: _____

        1. This is a face reflecting _____ .

        2. This is a face characterized by:

- Strong Conviction
- Courageous Moral Choices
- A Servant's Spirit
- Righteous Leadership

        3. This face is seen in Scripture:

> _"But the path of the righteous is like the light of dawn,_
> _That shines brighter and brighter until the full day."_
> —Proverbs 4:18

> _"A righteous man who walks in his integrity—_
> _How blessed are his sons after him."_ —Proverbs 20:7

    B. FACE TWO: _____

        1. This is a face reflecting _____ .

        2. This is a face characterized by:

- Initiating
- Protecting
- Providing
- Persevering
- Fighting

3. This face is seen in Scripture:

> "*...pursue righteousness, godliness, faith, love, perseverance and gentleness. Fight the good fight of faith; take hold of the eternal life to which you were called.*"
> —1 Timothy 6:11b-12a

C. FACE THREE: _____

1. This is a face reflecting _____.
2. This is a face characterized by:

- Tenderness
- Sensitivity
- Sacrificial care
- Emotional openness
- Physical affection

3. This face is seen in Scripture:

> "*Husbands, love your wives, just as Christ also loved the church and gave Himself up for her.*"
> —Ephesians 5:25

D. FACE FOUR: _____

1. This is a face reflecting _____.
2. This is a face characterized by:

- Loyalty
- Accountability
- Challenge
- Fun

3. This face is seen in Scripture:

> "*A friend loves at all times, And a brother is born for adversity.*" —Proverbs 17:17

> "*Iron sharpens iron, So one man sharpens another.*"
> —Proverbs 27:17

II. SOME IMPORTANT OBSERVATIONS ABOUT THESE FOUR FACES

A. ALL TOO OFTEN, THESE HONORABLE FACES OF
MANHOOD ARE REPLACED BY _____
CARICATURES.

← KING →

← LOVER →

← FRIEND →

← WARRIOR →

B. OUR INCREASINGLY FEMINIZED CULTURE HAS
EMASCULATED THE _____ IN MANY YOUNG
MEN. THE RESULT HAS BEEN THE CREATION OF
THE _____, INDECISIVE AS TO DIRECTION,
_____ AS TO LEADERSHIP.

C. OUR WORLD IS DESPERATE FOR THE _____
BALANCE OF REAL MANHOOD!

LET'S TALK IT OVER

Your 30 Minute Father-Son Debrief

☐ (Dads/Sons) In today's world, who (friends, public figures, fictional characters) do you know that wears …

The King's face well? _____

The Warrior's face well? _____

The Lover's face well? _____

The Friend's face well? _____

☐ (Sons) Which face do you think your age group wears the most? Why?

☐ (Dads) Which face do you think your age group wears the most? Why?

☐ (Dads) With which of these four faces have you had the most success in your life? Explain how wearing this face has helped advance your life as a man.

☐ (Dads) If you could live life over, which of the four faces would you have liked to have worn more or worn better? Explain why and how you think the lack of wearing this face has hurt your life as a man.

☐ (Sons) What one thing from this opening session had the most impact on you? Explain.

☐ (Dads/Sons) What is one practical thing you will leave with from today's session? Explain.

GENESIS AND MANHOOD, PART I

I. THE GENESIS "MYTH"

    A. MYTH IS NOT SYNONYMOUS WITH _____.

    B. A REAL MYTH EXPLAINS AND MEASURES OUR

        _____.

    C. THE "MYTH" OF GENESIS EXPLAINS AND MEASURES

        _____, BOTH IN ITS ORIGINAL _____

        AND IN ITS ONGOING _____.

    D. GENESIS DESCRIBES OUR ANCESTRAL

        _____.

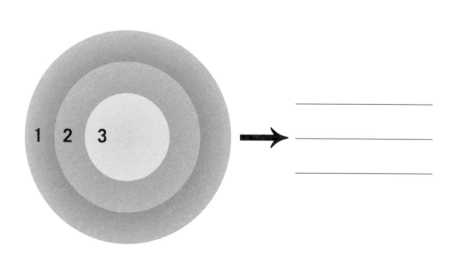

II. WHAT GENESIS 1 SAYS ABOUT MANHOOD.

A. IT SPEAKS OF MALE AND FEMALE _____ .

*Then God said, "Let Us make man in Our image, according to
Our likeness; and let them rule over the fish of the sea and over
the birds of the sky and over the cattle and over all the earth,
and over every creeping thing that creeps on the earth." And God
created man in His own image, in the image of God He created
him; male and female He created them.*
—Genesis 1:26-27

    1. Image
    2. Equally endowed/equally valuable
    3. Unique and special

B. IT SPEAKS OF MALE AND FEMALE _____ .

*And God blessed them; and God said to them, "Be fruitful and
multiply, and fill the earth, and subdue it; and rule over the fish
of the sea and over the birds of the sky, and over every
living thing that moves on the earth."* —Genesis 1:28

    1. Be fruitful/multiply/fill the earth
    2. Subdue the earth
    3. Rule over the earth

C. IT "HINTS" AT A VERY IMPORTANT SOCIAL _____ .

*Then God said, "Let Us make man in Our image, according to
Our likeness; and let them rule over the fish of the sea and over
the birds of the sky and over the cattle and over all the earth,
and over every creeping thing that creeps on the earth." And God
created man in His own image, in the image of God He created
him; male and female He created them.*
—Genesis 1:26-27

*He created them male and female, and He blessed them and
named them Man in the day when they were created.*
—Genesis 5:2

III. WHAT GENESIS 2 SAYS ABOUT MANHOOD

A. NOTICE: ADAM WAS CREATED _____ .

Then the LORD God formed man of dust from the ground, and breathed into his nostrils the breath of life; and man became a living being. —Genesis 2:7

B. NOTICE: ADAM IS GIVEN AN _____
AND _____ BEFORE EVE'S CREATION.

Then the LORD God took the man and put him into the garden of Eden to cultivate it and keep it. —Genesis 2:15

C. NOTICE: ADAM IS INSTRUCTED BY GOD WITH THE
RESPONSIBILITY OF _____ WITH HIS_____ .

And the LORD God commanded the man, saying, "From any tree of the garden you may eat freely; but from the tree of the knowledge of good and evil you shall not eat, for in the day that you eat from it you shall surely die." —Genesis 2:16-17

D. NOTICE: ADAM _____ THE ANIMALS, A SIGNAL OF
HIS LEADERSHIP OVER _____ .

And out of the ground the LORD God formed every beast of the field and every bird of the sky, and brought them to the man to see what he would call them; and whatever the man called a living creature, that was its name. —Genesis 2:19

E. NOTICE: ADAM IS GIVEN A "_____,"
A TITLE THAT OFFERS FURTHER EVIDENCE OF GOD'S
ORIGINAL CORE SOCIAL IDENTITY FOR THE MAN AND THE
WOMAN.

Then the LORD God said, "It is not good for the man to be alone; I will make him a helper suitable for him." —Genesis 2:18

LET'S TALK IT OVER

Your 30 Minute Father-Son Debrief

☐ (Dads/Sons) Are there any "real myths" that you measure your life by today? Who are they? What do you look up to in them?

☐ (Sons) What did you learn from Genesis that you did not know before? Explain.

☐ (Dads) What new insights on manhood did you receive today from Genesis? Explain.

☐ (Dads) How does what you heard from Genesis make you feel as a man: Good? Challenged? Not so good? Explain.

☐ (Sons) What impacted you the most from today's session? Explain.

☐ (Dads/Sons) What's one practical concept you will leave with from today's session? Explain.

1 4

GENESIS & MANHOOD, PART II

I. A BRIEF REVIEW

Male _____ is a personal moral _____, not a teaching of the Bible.

II. WHAT GENESIS 2 SAYS ABOUT MANHOOD

(continued from last week)

A. NOTICE: ADAM _____ HIS HELPER.

And the man said, "This is now bone of my bones, and flesh of my flesh; She shall be called Woman, Because she was taken out of Man." —Genesis 2:23

B. NOTICE: IT IS THE MAN WHO IS TOLD TO LEAVE AND _____ A NEW HOUSEHOLD.

For this cause a man shall leave his father and his mother, and shall cleave to his wife; and they shall become one flesh. —Genesis 2:24

III. WHAT GENESIS 3 SAYS ABOUT MANHOOD

A. NOTICE: THE TEMPTATION SEEKS TO _____ AND _____ GOD'S ORIGINAL SOCIAL AND SPIRITUAL ORDER.

Now the serpent was more crafty than any beast of the field which the LORD God had made. And he said to the woman, "Indeed, has God said, 'You shall not eat from any tree of the garden'?" And the woman said to the serpent, "From the fruit of the trees of the garden we may eat; but from the fruit of the tree which is in the middle of the garden, God has said, 'You shall not eat from it or touch it, lest you die.'" And the serpent said to the woman, "You surely shall not die! For God knows that in the day you eat from it your eyes will be opened, and you will be like God, knowing good and evil." When the woman saw that the tree was good for food, and that it was a delight to the eyes, and that the tree was desirable to make one wise, she took from its fruit and ate; and she gave also to her husband with her, and he ate. —Genesis 3:1-6

B. NOTICE: GOD HOLDS _____, NOT THE _____, ACCOUNTABLE FOR THIS FIRST SIN.

And they heard the sound of the LORD God walking in the garden in the cool of the day, and the man and his wife hid themselves from the presence of the LORD God among the trees of the garden. Then the LORD God called to the man, and said to him, "Where are you?" —Genesis 3:8-9

C. NOTICE: ADAM'S SIN HAS AN UNACCEPTABLE _____ ATTACHED TO IT.

And He said, "Who told you that you were naked? Have you eaten from the tree of which I commanded you not to eat?" And the man said, "The woman whom Thou gavest to be with me, she gave me from the tree, and I ate." —Genesis 3:11-12

D. NOTICE: ADAM'S CURSE IS BASED ON THE _____ OF GOD'S ORIGINAL CREATED ORDER.

Then to Adam He said, "Because you have listened to the voice of your wife, and have eaten from the tree about which I commanded you, saying, 'You shall not eat from it'; Cursed is the ground because of you; in toil you will eat of it All the days of your life." —Genesis 3:17

(Eve's curse is also based on her usurping God's created order.)

E. NOTICE: ADAM'S SIN UNLEASHES THE DESTRUCTIVE CURSE OF MALE _____.

"... he shall rule over you." —Genesis 3:16b

F. NOTICE: ADAM DIES.

And the LORD God commanded the man, saying, "From any tree of the garden you may eat freely; but from the tree of the knowledge of good and evil you shall not eat, for in the day that you eat from it you shall surely die." —Genesis 2:16-17

This judgment of _____ also extends to all those who come after him. He, not Eve, is _____ with the fall of the human race. Our depraved natures are due to Adam's sin.

For as through the one man's disobedience the many were made sinners, even so through the obedience of the One the many will be made righteous. —Romans 5:19

G. NOTICE: ADAM _____ HIS WIFE AS A CONTINUED SIGN OF HIS LEADERSHIP EVEN AFTER THE FALL.

Now the man called his wife's name Eve, because she was the mother of all the living. —Genesis 3:20

LET'S TALK IT OVER

Your 30 Minute Father-Son Debrief

☐ (Dads/Sons) React to the statement "Male domination is a personal moral failure, not a teaching of the Bible." Do men dominate women today? In what ways?

☐ (Sons) What did you learn from Genesis today that you did not know before? Were there any surprises? Explain.

☐ (Dads) What sense of increased masculine responsibility did you receive from the truths of Genesis 2 and 3? Explain.

☐ (Sons) What had the biggest impact on you from today's session? How was it helpful? Explain.

☐ (Dads) What is one truth from Genesis you would most want these sons to never forget? Why?

SESSION 4

¹⁸# THE TWO ADAMS OF MANHOOD

I. KEY REMINDERS

A. MEN WERE CREATED BY GOD TO BE _____
AND _____   _____.

   1. When men abandon this pursuit or when this pursuit is taken from them, _____   _____.

   2. We see this in Scripture:

> *For behold, the Lord GOD of hosts is going to remove from*
> *Jerusalem and Judah...*
> *The mighty man and the warrior,*
> *The judge and the prophet,*
> *The diviner and the elder,*
> *The captain of fifty and the honorable man,*
> *The counselor and the expert artisan,*
> *And the skillful enchanter.*
> *And I will make mere lads their princes,*
> *And capricious children will rule over them,*
> *And the people will be oppressed,*
> *Each one by another, and each one by his neighbor;*
> *The youth will storm against the elder*
> *And the inferior against the honorable.*
> *When a man lays hold of his brother in his father's house,*
> *saying,*
> *"You have a cloak, you shall be our ruler,*
> *And these ruins will be under your charge,"*
> *On that day will he protest, saying,*
> *"I will not be your healer,*
> *For in my house there is neither bread nor cloak;*
> *You should not appoint me ruler of the people."*
> *For Jerusalem has stumbled and Judah has fallen,*

*Because their speech and their actions are against the
LORD,
To rebel against His glorious presence.
The expression of their faces bears witness against them,
And they display their sin like Sodom;
They do not even conceal it
Woe to them!
For they have brought evil on themselves.
Say to the righteous that it will go well with them,
For they will eat the fruit of their actions.
Woe to the wicked! It will go badly with him,
For what he deserves will be done to him.
O My people! Their oppressors are children,
And women rule over them.* —Isaiah 3:1-12a

3. We see that today:

_____

_____

_____

_____

B. THE MALE LEADERSHIP OF GENESIS IS NOT NATURAL, BUT
_____ WITH SPECIFIC _____.

1. Will to _____.

2. Work to _____.

3. Woman to _____ and _____.

II. TWO MEN / TWO MASCULINE IDENTITIES

A. ADAM AND JESUS CHRIST

"Adam and Christ stand against each other as two great figures at the entrance of two worlds, two creations, the old and the new ... And in their actions and fates, lie the decisions for all who belong to them, because all men are comprehended in them."
—Theologian Hermann Ridderbos

B. THESE MEN ARE LEADERS OF TWO DISTINCT _____ DESTINIES FOR ALL HUMANITY.

For if by the transgression of the one, death reigned through the one, much more those who receive the abundance of grace and of the gift of righteousness will reign in life through the One, Jesus Christ. So then as through one transgression there resulted condemnation to all men, even so through one act of righteousness there resulted justification of life to all men. For as through the one man's disobedience the many were made sinners, even so through the obedience of the One the many will be made righteous. —Romans 5:17-19

C. THESE MEN ARE ALSO LEADERS OF TWO DISTINCT MASCULINE _____.

So also it is written, "The first MAN, Adam, BECAME A LIVING SOUL." The last Adam became a life-giving spirit. However, the spiritual is not first, but the natural; then the spiritual. The first man is from the earth, earthy; the second man is from heaven. As is the earthy, so also are those who are earthy; and as is the heavenly, so also are those who are heavenly. And just as we have borne the image of the earthy, we shall also bear the image of the heavenly. —1 Corinthians 15:45-49 _____

    1. The first Adam represents a manhood:
- Set on a natural _____.
- Based on personal instinct, human reason and reaction, not_____!
- That draws life from _____.
- Without _____ meaning.
- A living soul, "_____."

2. The second Adam represents a manhood:
- Set on a heavenly _____.
- Yielded to _____, not personal instinct, human reason, or reaction.
- That _____ others.
- Full of _____ meaning.
- "A life-giving _____."

D. HOW THESE TWO MASCULINE IDENTITIES PLAY OUT PRACTICALLY

ADAM'S MANHOOD BECOMES ...	JESUS' MANHOOD BECOMES ...
_____	_____
which focuses on:	which focuses on:
1. What a man _____	1. What a man _____
2._____ with other men	2._____ with other men
3. _____ power	3. _____ purpose
4. _____ rewards	4. _____ rewards
5. _____	5. _____
6. _____	6. _____

III. DEFINING DIFFERENCES BETWEEN ADAM AND CHRIST

A. THE FIRST ADAM FELL INTO _____; THE SECOND ADAM (CHRIST)_____ _____.

1. *When the woman saw that the tree was good for food, and that it was a delight to the eyes, and that the tree was desirable to make one wise, she took from its fruit and ate; and she gave also to her husband with her, and he ate.* —Genesis 3:6

2. *... although He existed in the form of God, did not regard equality with God a thing to be grasped, but emptied Himself, taking the form of a bond-servant, and being made in the likeness of men. And being found in appearance as a man, He humbled Himself by becoming obedient to the point of death, even death on a cross.* —Philippians 2:6-8

B. REAL MEN _____

LET'S TALK IT OVER

Your 30 Minute Father-Son Debrief

☐ (Dads/Sons) React to the following statement: "Men are leading less and less today; women are leading more and more." Agree? Disagree? Explain.

☐ (Dads/Sons) Look again at Isaiah 3:1-12a. What one statement in these verses stands out for you? Why?

☐ (Dads) This session addresses two Adams and two distinct masculinities. Where have you seen aspects of the first Adam's manhood in your life? Explain.

☐ (Dads) Where have you seen aspects of the second Adam's (Jesus) manhood in your life? Explain.

☐ (Sons) What was the most important thing you heard in today's session? Why?

☐ (Dads) Where have you seen Adam's passivity in your own life and marriage? Explain.

☐ (Dads) If you could change one thing about your manhood right now, what would it be? Explain.

2 4

A BIBLICAL DEFINITION OF MANHOOD

I. THE FOUR DIFFERENCES BETWEEN ADAM AND CHRIST

A. THE FIRST ADAM FELL INTO _____;
THE SECOND ADAM _____.

B. THE FIRST ADAM DISREGARDED HIS RESPONSIBILITIES;
THE SECOND ADAM _____ _____.

1. He accepted responsibility:

- For a _____ to obey.
- For a _____ to do.
- For a _____ to love.

2. What causes a man to accept social and spiritual responsibility?

- When it is clear from a young age that the primary responsibility for the social/spiritual well being of others (namely wife, children) rests _____.
- When he has been trained from an early age by the men in his life to _____ and _____ these responsibilities.
- When he is _____, especially by other men, for accepting these _____.
- When he has been spiritually transformed in the heart by Jesus Christ to _____ these responsibilities in order to _____ God.

C. THE FIRST ADAM ABANDONED HIS POST OF LEADERSHIP;
THE SECOND ADAM CHOSE TO _____ _____ .

1. Men were created to _____, but it takes
_____.

2. Jesus led where Adam didn't:
   - He set _____.
   - He provided _____.
   - He made _____.

3. To be a courageous leader, every man must master one
significant obstacle: _____

D. THE FIRST ADAM SOUGHT A GREATER REWARD; THE SEC-
OND ADAM _____ .

1. Examples of second-Adam living:
   - (Jesus) *Therefore, since we have so great a cloud of
     witnesses surrounding us, let us also lay aside every
     encumbrance, and the sin which so easily entangles us,
     and let us run with endurance the race that is set before
     us, fixing our eyes on Jesus, the author and perfecter of
     faith, who for the joy set before Him endured the cross,
     despising the shame, and has sat down at the right hand
     of the throne of God.* —Hebrews 12:1-2

   - (David) *I would have despaired unless I had believed
     that I would see the goodness of the LORD In the land of
     the living.* —Psalm 27:13

   - (Moses) *By faith Moses, when he had grown up, refused
     to be called the son of Pharaoh's daughter; choosing
     rather to endure ill-treatment with the people of God
     than to enjoy the passing pleasures of sin; considering
     the reproach of Christ greater riches than the treasures
     of Egypt; for he was looking to the reward.*
     —Hebrews 11:24-26

- (Paul) *I have fought the good fight, I have finished the course, I have kept the faith; in the future there is laid up for me the crown of righteousness, which the Lord, the righteous Judge, will award to me on that day; and not only to me, but also to all who have loved His appearing.* —2 Timothy 4:7-8

2. Exhortations to second Adam living:
   - *...bodily discipline is only of little profit, but godliness is profitable for all things, since it holds promise for the present life and also for the life to come.* —1 Timothy 4:8

   - *And without faith it is impossible to please Him, for he who comes to God must believe that He is and that He is a rewarder of those who seek Him.* —Hebrews 11:6

II. WHAT IS A REAL MAN FROM A BIBLICAL MOLD?

A real man is one who ...

- Rejects _____
- Accepts _____
- Leads_____
- Expects the greater _____, _____ _____.

LET'S TALK IT OVER

Your 30 Minute Father-Son Debrief

☐ (Dads) Were you given (by your dad or someone else) a clear understanding of what it meant to "be a man" while growing up? If not, how did you define manhood for yourself? Explain.

☐ (Dads) Was it clear to you growing up what responsibilities you would need to embrace to be a real man? Did someone train you to skillfully assume these responsibilities? If so, how did that help you as a man in life? (In dating, marriage, work, money management, parenting, being the head of your home, spirituality, etc?) If not, how has that hurt you as a man? Explain.

☐ (Sons) Notice the definition of manhood given in this session has four parts. Which of those four components speaks to you the most? Why?

☐ (Dads) Which of the four components of the manhood definition speaks to you the most? Why?

☐ (Sons) What is the most important thing you heard in today's session and discussion? Explain.

☐ (Dads/Sons) How could the definition of manhood given today be used to draw a father and son closer together? In what specific ways? Explain.

SESSION 6

A MAN AND HIS LIFE JOURNEY

I. THE LIFE CYCLE MAP

    A. *SEASONS OF A MAN'S LIFE,* (Daniel Levinson, Ballantine Books, 1978)

    B. AN OVERVIEW:

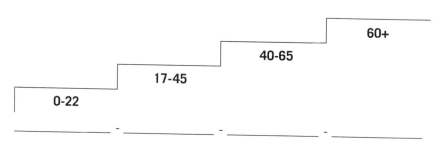

    C. THE FOUR SEASONS AND TRANSITIONS

        1. Spring

        2. Summer

        3. Fall

        4. Winter

II. THE LIFE STAGES MAP

A. *THE MASCULINE JOURNEY,* (Robert Hicks, NavPress 1993)

B. AN OVERVIEW

Zaken: The _____ Stage

Ish: The _____ Stage

Enosh: The _____ Stage

Gibbor: The _____ Stage

Zakar: The _____ Stage

Adam: The _____ Stage

C. THE SIX LIFE STAGES

1. The Creational Stage (0-20)
   a. Gifts and talents
   b. Acceptance and development, or confusion and missed opportunity

2. The Phallic Stage (13-25)
   a. Sexual energy
   b. Mastery or enslavement

3. The Warrior Stage (20-40)
   a. The drive to establish oneself
   b. Life in the fight

4. The Wounded Stage (40-50)
   a. Powerful re-evaluations
   b. Renewal or rut

5. The Mature Stage (50-60)
   a. Deeper meaning
   b. Strategic moves and mentoring

6. The Sage Stage (60+)
   a. Standard bearers
   b. Special contributions
   c. Leaving a legacy

III. CONCLUSION

LET'S TALK IT OVER

Your 30 Minute Father-Son Debrief

☐ (Dads/Sons) How do these maps help you? What insights do they offer you for your life right now? Explain.

☐ (Dads) Do these maps generally match up with what you have experienced in life? Explain.

☐ (Dads) Which "life stage" would you like to live over again if given the chance? Explain. What would you do differently? Why?

☐ (Sons) Which of the six "life stages" (other than the one you are in) do you most look forward to? Why?

☐ (Dads/Sons) What is the biggest overall benefit you will take from this six-session study? How do you think it will impact your life in the future? Explain.

☐ (Dads/Sons) What is one commitment you will make right now to better live as an authentic man? Explain.

More Resources from Men's Fraternity

IMAGINE THE TRANSFORMING POWER of men coming together in your church to honestly examine their lives and to take the courageous steps necessary to embrace authentic biblical manhood.

That is the goal of Men's Fraternity *(www.mensfraternity.com)*, a powerful ministry created by Robert Lewis, pastor-at-large of Fellowship Bible Church in Little Rock, Arkansas. Men's Fraternity is designed to foster true spiritual and emotional growth among men as they meet for weekly teaching sessions and small-group interaction. Each study is designed to engage the heart as well as the mind, stripping away the myths of manhood and focusing on how each individual can be transformed into a true man of God.

THE GREAT ADVENTURE

This 20-week study is designed to help men understand their true identity and to guide them to break free from the bondage of boredom to embark on the adventure of their lives.

DVD SET The 20 DVDs in this kit include teaching sessions by Robert Lewis, each with approximately 45 minutes of content. Church leaders can review this material and use it to create their own presentations or simply play the DVDs for the group. 1-4158-2296-4 • **$299.00**

VIEWER GUIDE This workbook allows participants to easily follow along with presentations and provides a guide for later review. Also includes questions to help spur small-group discussion. 1-4158-2290-5 • **$9.95**

AUDIO CD PACK Contains the audio portion of each session so that participants can review any sessions they miss. 1-4158-2291-3 • **$139.00**

WINNING AT WORK & HOME

As a man, are you looking for answers and seeking direction? This 16-week study will help you crack the code on what it means to be a real man. Discover how to win at work and at home, the two most critical areas of a man's life. Unlock the truth of authentic manhood and empower your everyday life!
DVD SET 1-4158-2823-7 • **$299.00**
VIEWER GUIDE 1-4158-2824-5 • **$9.95**
AUDIO CD PACK 1-4158-2822-9 • **$139.00**

Also From Robert Lewis
Raising a Modern-Day Knight Video Adventure Series
Based on the best-selling book, this six-part adventure series explores how dads can raise their sons into noble, vibrant masculinity and healthy manhood. Seven DVDs of instruction by Robert Lewis and Dennis Rainey, the book *Raising a Modern-Day Knight*, a leader guide, a training guide, and a legacy album equip men to connect with their sons and become effective and strategic fathers. For information visit www.rmdk.com.